CH00662889

JAMES RAE

EASY STUDIES IN

JAZZ & ROCK
SAXOPHONE

UNIVERSAL SAXOPHONE EDITION

www.universaledition.com

vienna · london · new york

UE 19 392

ISMN M-008-04537-0
UPC 8-03452-01095-1
ISBN 978-3-7024-1352-1

PREFACE

This album of Studies for Saxophone is a 'user friendly' introduction to Jazz and Rock phrasing at an elementary level. The book is divided into two sections, Jazz and Rock. In the Jazz pieces, all quavers are to be played in swingtime, (i.e. ♫ = ♩♪). In the Rock pieces they are as written, (straight!). This book can be used as an ideal primer for the more advanced '20 Modern Studies' also in this series.

James Rae

VORWORT

Diese Etüdensammlung für Saxophon ist eine „benutzerfreundliche" Einführung in die Grundlagen der Jazz- und Rockphrasierung. Der Band ist in einen Jazz- und einen Rockabschnitt unterteilt. In den Jazzetüden sind alle Achtelnoten im Swingrhythmus zu spielen (d.h. ♫ = ♩♪). In den Rocketüden müssen sie so gespielt werden, wie sie geschrieben stehen (gleichmäßig!). Dieser Band eignet sich ideal als Vorbereitung auf die anspruchsvolleren „20 Modern Studies", die ebenfalls in dieser Reihe erschienen sind.

James Rae

CONTENTS

JAZZ

JAMES RAE

1. Mayfair

2. Flapjack

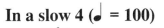

3. Leapfrog

Universal Edition UE 19 392

2

4. Freeway

5. Butterscotch

6. Over And Out

3

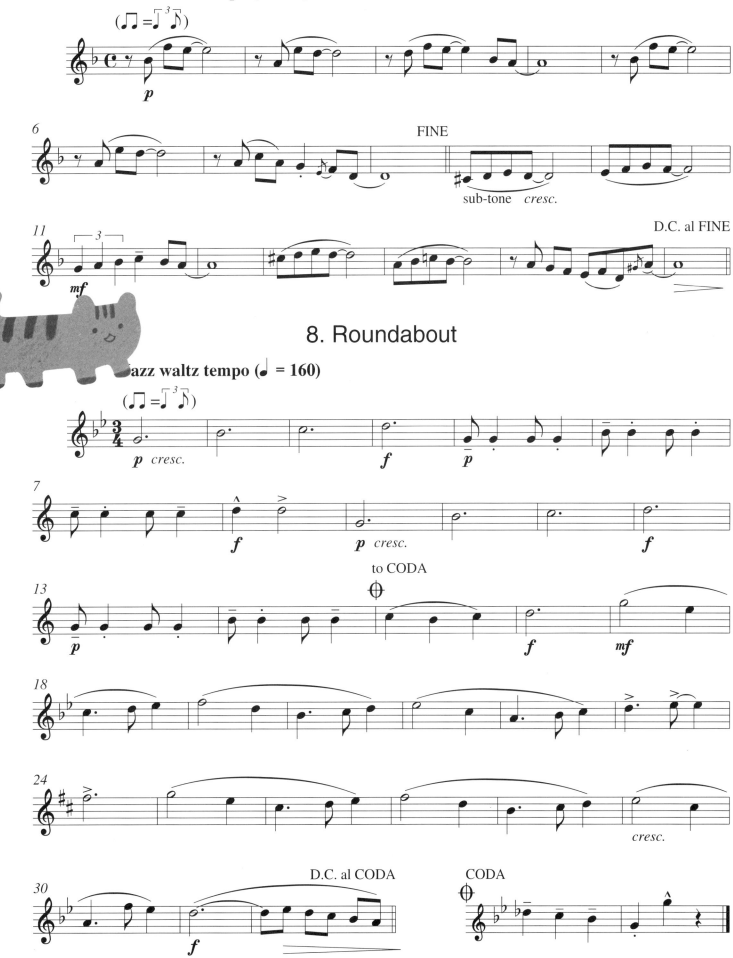

4

9. Band Room Blues

10. Ted's Shuffle

11. One Way Ticket

Slow blues tempo (♩ = 80)

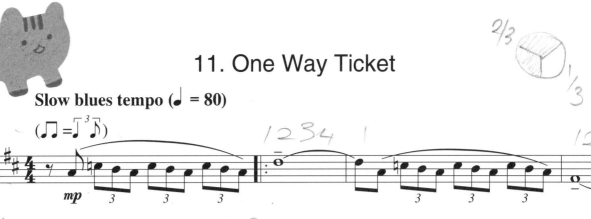

12. Movin'

Fast swing tempo (♩ = 200)

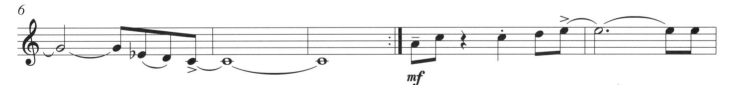

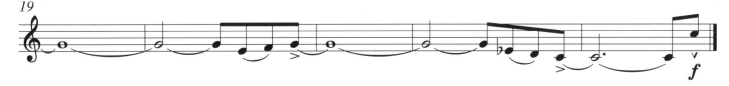

6

13. Last Orders

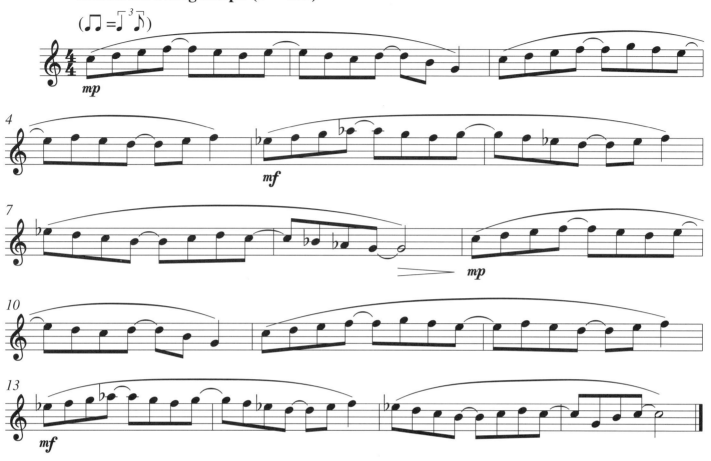

14. Yo-Yo

15. Fifth Gear

ROCK

8

16. First Take

Steady rock tempo (♩ = 108)

17. Power Plant

Slow and heavy (♩ = 88)

18. Discomatic

Moderate rock tempo (♩ = 104)

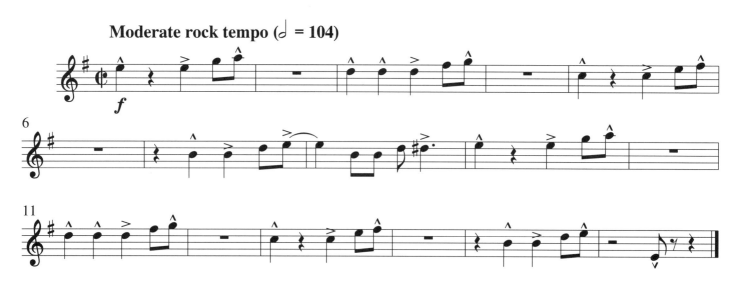

19. Underpass

Hard rock beat (♩ = 92)

f aggressive

20. Sir Neville

Steady rock tempo (♩ = 82)

to CODA

dal 𝄋 al CODA   CODA

21. Overdrive

Fast rock tempo (♩ = 144)

loud!

22. No Return

Heavy, in a slow 4 (♩ = 80)

FINE

dal 𝄋 al FINE

23. In the Beginning

Moderately (♩ = 100)

24. Road Hog

In a steady 2 (♩. = 132)

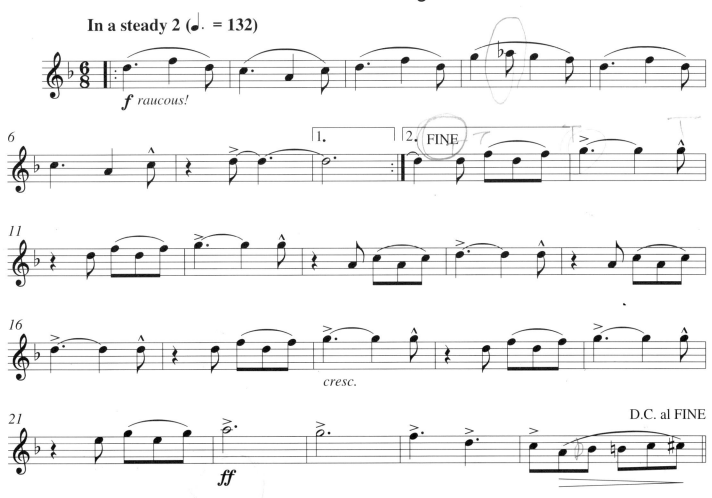

12

25. Work-Out

Steady rock tempo (♩ = 88)

26. Windy Ridge

Steady funk tempo (♩ = 100)

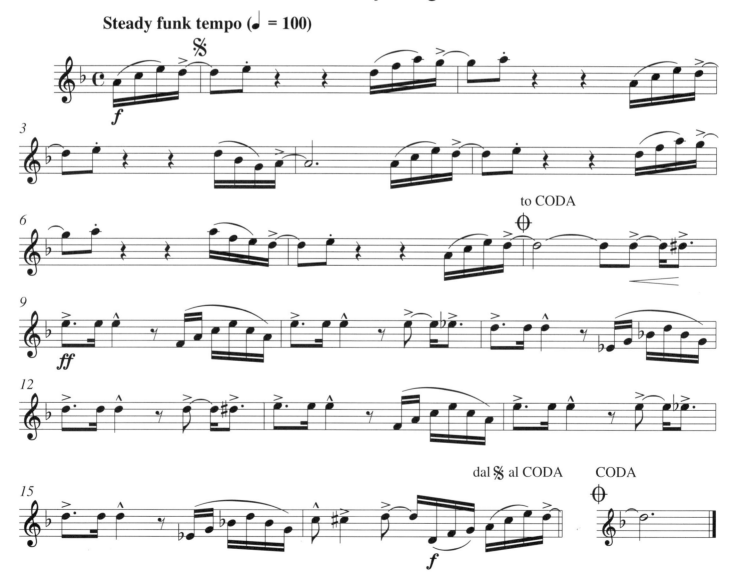

A selection of saxophone titles by James Rae

Easy

Introducing the Saxophone Plus Book 1 (alto sax & pno)	UE 30 420
Eyes & Ears Saxophone Level 1 – Sight-reading (2 sax)	UE 21 144
Easy Blue Saxophone (alto or tenor sax & pno)	UE 21 262
Easy Jazzy Saxophone (alto or tenor sax & pno)	UE 16 578
Easy Jazzy Duets (2 sax)	UE 16 551
Play it Cool – Saxophone (alto or tenor sax & pno or CD)	UE 21 100
Easy Studies in Jazz and Rock (sax)	UE 19 392

Easy to Intermediate

Introducing the Saxophone (Engl.) (alto sax + CD)	UE 17 390
James Rae's Methode für Saxophon (Dt.) (Altsax.+ CD)	UE 31 499
Introducing the Saxophone Plus Book 2 (alto sax & pno)	UE 30 421
Introducing Saxophone – Duets (2 sax)	UE 21 359
Introducing Saxophone – Trios (3 sax)	UE 21 360
Introducing Saxophone – Quartets (4 sax)	UE 21 361
Eyes & Ears Saxophone Level 2 – Sight-reading (2 sax)	UE 21 145
Style Workout – Saxophone (sax)	UE 21 232
20 Modern Studies (sax)	UE 18 820
Latin Saxophone (alto or tenor sax & pno)	UE 17 364
Jazz Zone (alto or tenor sax + CD)	UE 21 030
Sounds Irish (alto or tenor sax & pno)	UE 21 080

Intermediate

Blue Saxophone (alto or tenor sax & pno)	UE 19 765
Jazzy Saxophone 1 (alto or tenor sax & pno)	UE 18 827
Jazzy Saxophone 2 (alto or tenor sax & pno)	UE 19 362
Jazzy Duets (2 sax)	UE 19 395

www.universaledition.com
vienna · london · new york

Universal Saxophone Edition

UE-Nr.

17 770   Easy Classical Studies / Leichte klassische Studien (John Harle)

17 771   Scales and Arpeggios, Part I / Tonleiterstudien, Teil I (John Harle)

17 775   Scales and Arpeggios, Part II / Tonleiterstudien, Teil II (John Harle)

17 772   Classical Album / Klassische Spielstücke (John Harle)

17 774   Johann Sebastian BACH : Sonata G minor,
          BWV 1020,transcribed for saxophone and piano by John Harle

17 780   Johann Sebastian BACH: Two Preludes and Fugues BWV 857 and BWV 885
          transcribed for saxophone quartet by Reinhard Huuck

17 773   Richard Rodney BENNETT: Conversations / Zwiegespräche for 2 saxophones

17 447   Luciano BERIO: Sequenza IXb per sassofono contralto

17 777   Claude DEBUSSY-Album for alto saxophone and piano arranged by James Rae

19 072   Claude DEBUSSY: Clair de lune,
          Ausgabe für Altsaxophon und Klavier bearbeitet von Heinz Stolba

17 778   George GERSHWIN: 3 Preludes arranged for saxophone quartet by W. Schlei

13 984   Frank MARTIN: Ballade pour saxophone (cor de basset) et orchestre.
          Réduction pour saxophone et piano par John Lenehan

17 776   Dominic MULDOWNEY: ... In a Hall of Mirrors ... for alto saxophone and piano

18 820   James RAE: 20 modern studies in rhythm and interpretation for solo saxophone

18 508   Erik SATIE: Saxophone Album
          arranged for alto saxophone and piano by James Rae

17 779   Wolfgang SCHLEI: Invention for saxophone quartet

18 836   Take Ten for alto saxophone arranged by James Rae

19 075   Antonio VIVALDI: Concerto Op. 3/6 (RV 356)
          arranged for E-flat saxophone by James Rae

17 575   Kurt WEILL: Music from the Threepenny Opera
          arranged for saxophone quartet by John Harle

17 747   Jacques WILDBERGER: Portrait pour saxophone alto en mi♭

10 024   Necil Kâzim AKSES: Allegro Feroce for alto saxophone in E flat and piano

This series will be continued / Die Reihe wird fortgesetzt

www.universaledition.com
vienna · london · new york

577/02 IV